WHAT NATION ARE YOU?

THIS ANNUAL BELONGS TO

Luca

AGE

8

FAVOURITE CHARACTER

Aang

EGMONT
We bring stories to life

First published in Great Britain 2010
by Egmont UK Limited
239 Kensington High Street, London W8 6SA
Text by Catherine Shoolbred.
Design by Candice Bekir.
© 2010 Paramount Pictures. All Rights Reserved.
The Last Airbender and all related titles, logos
and characters are trademarks of Viacom
International Inc.

ISBN 978 1 4052 5390 1
1 3 5 7 9 10 8 6 4 2
Printed in Italy

CONTENTS

He is the last of his kind, all that remains of a once powerful nation. Some think he is a myth, some believe he is the chosen one who will bring balance to a world at war. And some will stop at nothing to destroy him ...

Turn over to join the adventures of the last airbender!

THE STORY SO FAR…

In a lost age, the world is divided into four nations: the Water Tribes, the Earth Kingdom, the Fire Nation and the Air Nomads. In each, there are powerful men and women who can control the element of their nation. They are the waterbenders, earthbenders, firebenders and airbenders.

In every generation, only one person can control all four elements – he is the Avatar, the link between the human and spirit worlds. When he dies, his spirit is reborn into the next nation in the cycle, which keeps the world in harmony.

But one day, a comet zoomed across the sky and firebenders were given a moment of great power. The Fire Nation launched a war against the other nations. And just when the world needed the Avatar the most, he mysteriously vanished.

A hundred years have passed since the comet came and the Fire Nation is now close to final victory in its ruthless war. It has destroyed the Air Nomads. It has raided the Water Tribes and the Earth Kingdom and both nations fight endless battles against its forces. Most people believe that the Avatar was never reborn into the Air Nomads and all hope for the world has been lost.

In the freezing Southern Water Tribe, a lone village struggles to survive. Two years have passed since the men of the village left to fight the Fire Nation.

Fifteen-year-old Katara is the village's only remaining waterbender. One day she is hunting with her brother, Sokka, when they spot something glowing in the icy ground.

Sokka uses his boomerang to break a hole in the ice. The ground cracks apart and a glowing ice sphere bursts out! When Katara strikes it, a strong gust of wind knocks her and Sokka over, and a blinding white light flashes high into the sky.

When Sokka and Katara open their eyes, they see two figures lying on the ice – a young boy and a large creature.

They carry the unconscious boy to their village and the creature follows. The boy has a shaven head and unusual tattoos. When he wakes, he tells them his name is Aang and he ran away with Appa, his flying bison, because he was upset. Aang knows he should go home, so he picks up his staff to leave. But then a Fire Nation warship crashes onto the shore!

A teenager in Fire Nation uniform leads soldiers into the village. He is Prince Zuko, heir to the Fire Nation throne. He has a scar on his face where he has been burnt.

Fire Lord Ozai has sent Zuko, his son, on a mission to find the missing Avatar. Zuko believes the Avatar must be very old, as he's been missing for a hundred years, so he demands to see all the village elders.

Noticing Aang's unusual tattoos, Zuko asks his name. Aang won't tell him so he's taken prisoner. At first he refuses to go with the Fire Nation soldiers, but when the prince threatens to burn down the village, Aang agrees to leave to protect his friends.

Sokka and Katara are determined to help Aang. They can't catch up with the warship in their canoe, but Appa will fly them to the rescue!

As Katara and Sokka turn to go, their grandmother tells them that Aang's tattoos are those of an airbender, and they haven't been seen in over a century. She believes Aang is the missing Avatar and it's Katara and Sokka's destiny to help him bring peace to the world. They hug Grandma goodbye and quickly set off on their great adventure!

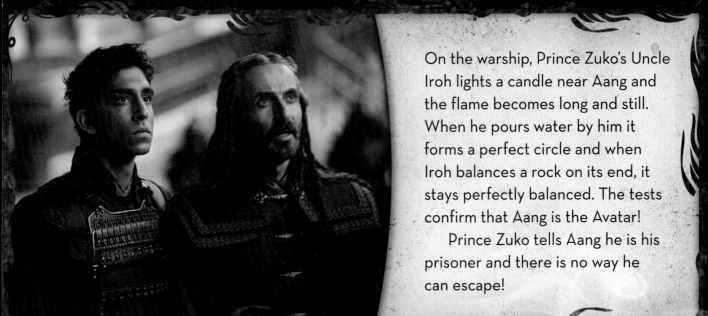

On the warship, Prince Zuko's Uncle Iroh lights a candle near Aang and the flame becomes long and still. When he pours water by him it forms a perfect circle and when Iroh balances a rock on its end, it stays perfectly balanced. The tests confirm that Aang is the Avatar!

Prince Zuko tells Aang he is his prisoner and there is no way he can escape!

Aang bends the air, making a gust of wind that sucks him out of the room and slams the door, locking Iroh and Zuko in! Aang holds off the guards as he grabs his staff and hurries up to the deck.

He smiles as he sees Katara and Sokka floating nearby on Appa. He shakes his staff and wings appear on the sides. Then he leaps off the ship with his staff and glides into the air to freedom!

Prince Zuko is furious that he underestimated the Avatar. His uncle believes that Zuko and the Avatar's destinies are tied, which is why Zuko saw the bright light that led them to him. Zuko is determined to capture the Avatar again, but he wonders where he has been all this time.

Turn to page 18 where the Avatar is revealed!

PROFILE: AANG

STRENGTHS:
As the Avatar, Aang has the ability to bend all four elements, but so far he's only learned to bend air. He is the last surviving airbender and the fate of the world rests on his shoulders — quite a responsibility for a thirteen-year-old!

WEAKNESSES:
He needs master tutors to teach him to bend water, earth and fire, so he is strong enough to end the war.

FRIENDS:
He is devastated to find that his Air Nomad friends have died, but he becomes firm friends with Katara and Sokka, and he loves his flying bison, Appa.

Colour in this picture of Aang, using the smaller picture as a guide.

Get your brain in gear by answering the questions in the grid. Then rearrange the letters in the blue boxes to reveal a name.

1 What was Aang frozen in? (3,6)

2 What is on Prince Zuko's face? (4)

3 Which element can Katara bend? (5)

4 What is the name of Aang's flying creature? (4)

5 Aang is the last ----------. (9)

6 What is Zuko's uncle called? (4)

7 Who gave Katara her necklace? (6)

8 Prince Zuko's father is Fire ---- ----. (4,4)

9 What does Aang have on his head? (6)

10 What is Katara's brother called? (5)

The hidden name is:

PROFILE: KATARA

STRENGTHS:

Katara is focused and practises waterbending every day. She is determined to help Aang bring peace to the world. Her mother's necklace gives her courage when she needs it most.

WEAKNESSES:

Her waterbending skills are limited — she often soaks or freezes her brother by mistake! She needs to be taught by a master waterbender, who can help uncover her full potential.

FRIENDS:

She loves her tribe and family, and cares for and protects her new best friend, Aang.

Appa flies to Aang's home, the Southern Air Temple where he lived with the Air Nomads. Katara realises Aang doesn't know that a hundred years have passed while he was frozen in the ice.

Aang thinks his friends will be in the prayer field, so he rushes there eagerly to greet them.

The prayer field is covered in bones and the signs of an ancient war. Aang is horrified to see the necklace he made for his tutor lying around a skeleton's neck.

Katara gently explains that the Fire Nation killed all the Air Nomads because they knew the Avatar had been born into that nation and wanted to destroy him. Aang is the last airbender!

As Aang cries for his lost friends, his emotions create a powerful wind that lifts him into the air and his mind enters the spirit world. The Dragon Spirit tells him that the human and spirit worlds are in trouble. "Where have you been?" he says. "You may already be too late!"

When Aang returns to the human world, he hears Katara calling to him, saying, "I know you feel alone. Sokka and I can be your family. I'm your friend. I won't leave you!"

Aang floats back to the ground and hugs her.

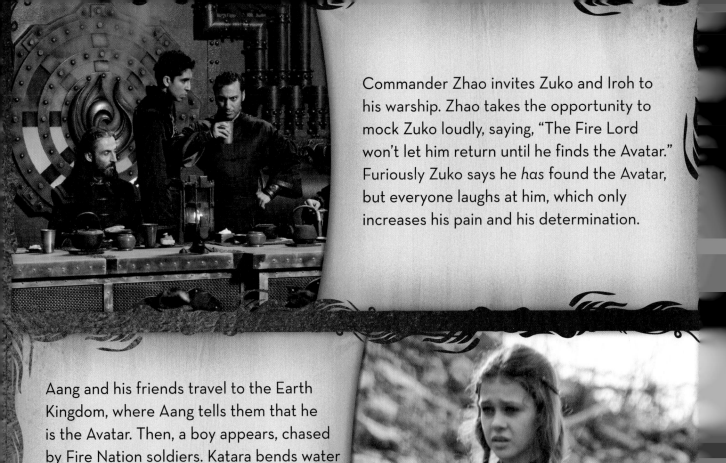

Commander Zhao invites Zuko and Iroh to his warship. Zhao takes the opportunity to mock Zuko loudly, saying, "The Fire Lord won't let him return until he finds the Avatar." Furiously Zuko says he *has* found the Avatar, but everyone laughs at him, which only increases his pain and his determination.

Aang and his friends travel to the Earth Kingdom, where Aang tells them that he is the Avatar. Then, a boy appears, chased by Fire Nation soldiers. Katara bends water at them, but accidentally freezes Sokka!

They are all taken to an Earth Kingdom prison. Sokka realises all the prisoners are earthbenders. The Fire Nation is trying to stop the benders of all other nations, so that firebenders can control the world!

Aang tells the earthbender prisoners that he is the Avatar. "You are powerful and amazing people. You don't need to live like this!" he shouts.

The Fire Nation guards think that all airbenders were killed, so they don't believe Aang. But when a guard grabs Katara, Aang uses his abilities to free her. The prisoners come to Aang's defence and start earthbending to fight off the guards. The soldiers are overwhelmed and flee – leaving the villagers to celebrate their freedom!

Turn to page 56 to learn about Aang's past ...

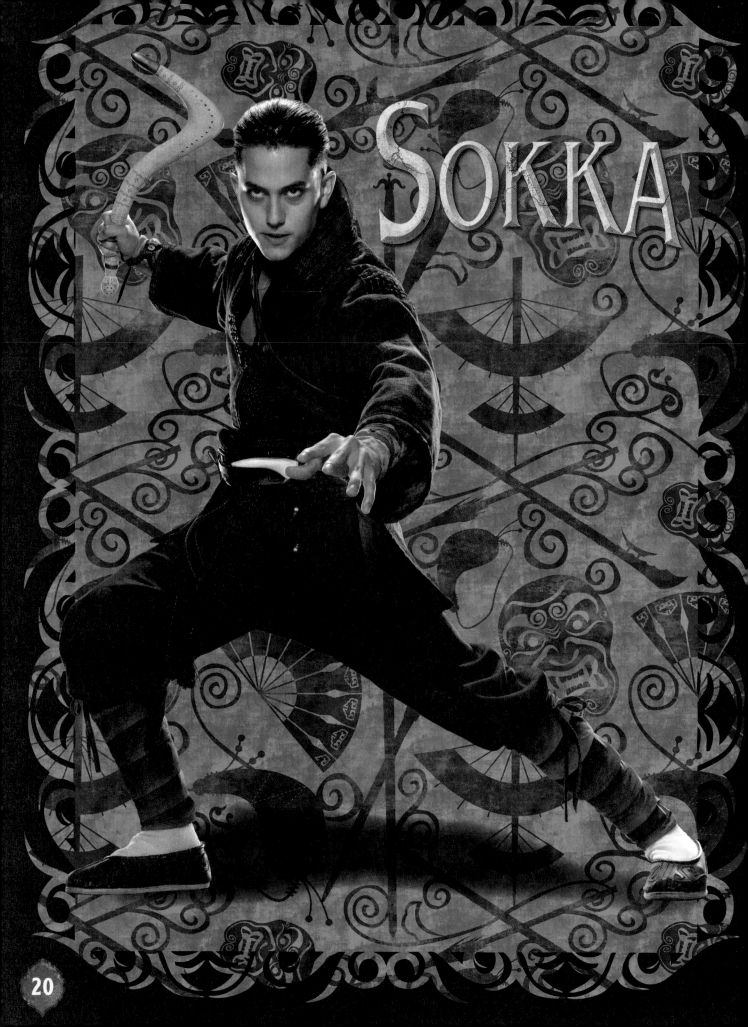

SOKKA

PROFILE: SOKKA

WATER TRIBE

STRENGTHS:
Loyal and courageous, he has the strength and determination of a warrior. At seventeen, he lacks experience, but he always finds clever ways to get out of trouble.

WEAKNESSES:
He doesn't have the ability to bend water, and is often the victim of his sister's waterbending efforts.

FRIENDS:
He is protective of his sister, Katara, and his friend, Aang. He forms a very close bond with Princess Yue of the Northern Water Tribe.

Take the letters shown from each character and write them in the box below. Then unjumble them to spell one of the four elements.

KATARA
(3rd letter)

PRINCE ZUKO
(6th letter)

UNCLE IROH
(9th letter)

LORD OZAI
(3rd letter)

AANG
(2nd letter)

The element is:

TO THE RESCUE

Aang needs to master all four elements before he can defeat the Fire Nation. But which element should he use to get to the Northern Water Tribe?

HOW TO PLAY:
Starting at the different elements, move the number shown in the direction on the arrows to see which one leads him to the Northern Water Tribe.

AIR
FIRE
WATER
EARTH

NORTHERN
WATER
TRIBE

PRINCE ZUKO

PROFILE: PRINCE ZUKO

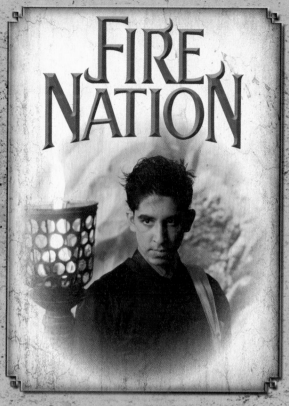

STRENGTHS:
Focused and determined, this teenage firebender is obsessed with capturing the Avatar and regaining his honour and position as heir to the throne.

WEAKNESSES:
He's an intimidating bully who believes firebending can never be outdone by water, earth or airbending. He thinks he is invincible, and charges into things without thinking.

FRIENDS:
He has more enemies than friends! His father, Fire Lord Ozai, has banished him from the throne, but his Uncle Iroh is always there to protect and advise him.

Aang is taking on Prince Zuko in a battle.
Write your own scores in the character's boxes,
then add them up to see who wins!

ABILITY

10 **/10**

GOODNESS

9.5 **/10**

OUTFIT

9.5 **/10**

WILL TO WIN

10 **/10**

TOTAL

39 **/40**

ABILITY

9.5 /10

GOODNESS

1.5 /10

OUTFIT

9.5 /10

WILL TO WIN

10 /10

TOTAL

31.5 /40

Prince Zuko is heir to the Fire Nation. How many small flames can you find on these pages?

EYE FOR DETAIL

Can you spot these details in the big picture of Sokka and Katara?
Add a tick in the boxes below as you find each one.

HIT THE TARGETS

Look at the page carefully then shut your eyes. Then use a pencil to try to draw a dot on all six targets. Open your eyes to add up the numbers on the targets you hit to reveal your score!

1 2 3 4 3 2 1

1 2 3 4 3 2 1

1 2 3 4 3 2 1

1 2 3 4 3 2 1

1 2 3 4 3 2 1

1 2 3 4 3 2 1

0-7   YOU LACK FOCUS
8-15   YOU HAVE POTENTIAL
16-24   AVATAR LEVEL

YOUR SCORE:

Use the code below to reveal Prince Zuko's secret message.
Write the letters in the boxes below.

A B C D E F G H I J K L M

N O P Q R S T U V W X Y Z

ZUKO'S SECRET MESSAGE:

I must

Find The

avatar

SOKKA

KATARA

A-MAZE-ING MAZE

Help Aang get through the maze to find Katara and Sokka.
You need to avoid any Fire Nation flames on the way!

START

FINISH

Use the code to find out who is being watched by the Fire Nation.
Then draw lines to match each name to the correct picture.

A

1

B
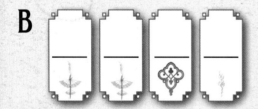

2

C
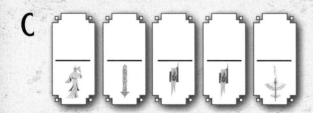

3

D
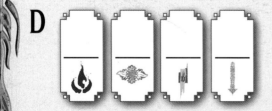

4

COLOUR ZUKO

Give Prince Zuko some colour to complete this picture of him in his Fire Nation uniform.

FIRE LORD OZAI

Profile: Fire Lord Ozai

STRENGTHS:
He is the leader of the Fire Nation and commander-in-chief of the war. Having defeated a large part of the other nations, Fire Lord Ozai now wishes to conquer the spirit world as well.

WEAKNESSES:
This brutal and battle-hungry leader thinks he's invincible, but his ruthless cruelty might lead people to pledge their loyalty elsewhere.

FRIENDS:
He doesn't want friends! Instead he uses violence and fear to get his way. He even banished his own son and sent him on an almost impossible quest to find the Avatar.

FIND THE TRUE AVATAR

There is only one true Avatar.

Can you spot him hidden amongst these imposters?

ZUKO

SOKKA

Which one of these silhouettes is really Sokka?

Circle him when you find the true warrior.

UNCLE IROH

PROFILE: UNCLE IROH

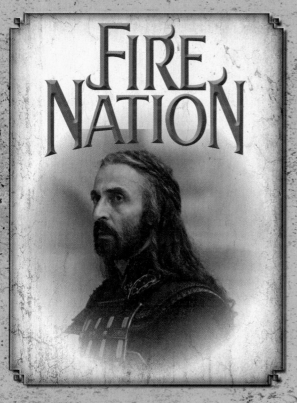

STRENGTHS:
This wise man was once a great general. He is easy-going and a good advisor to his nephew, Prince Zuko. He turns out to be a powerful firebender.

WEAKNESSES:
Now in his mature years, he's not the warrior he once was. He doesn't have the ruthless streak of other Fire Nation leaders, but this helps him be a good person.

FRIENDS:
Once a high-ranking Fire Nation general, Iroh gave up power and the throne to his younger brother, Fire Lord Ozai. He now prefers to spend his time with a few loyal friends and acting as a father figure to his nephew, Prince Zuko.

MIND-BENDING QUIZ

1) Where does Princess Yue rule?

a. Eastern Water Tribe
b. Western Water Tribe
c. Northern Water Tribe
d. Southern Water Tribe

2) As the Avatar, what two worlds does Aang connect?

a. the human and spirit worlds
b. the animal and spirit worlds
c. the human and magical worlds
d. the magical and spirit worlds

3) Why did Aang run away from home?

a. he wanted to join the circus
b. he was angry that he couldn't have a family
c. he wanted to travel the world
d. he didn't want to do his chores

4) Suki's warriors help Aang complete his journey. What are they called?

a. Kyoshi Warriors
b. Karate Warriors
c. Kaboshi Warriors
d. Kendo Warriors

5) Which three skills does Aang still need to master?

a. waterbending, earthbending and firebending
b. rainbending, earthbending and airbending
c. earthbending, firebending and airbending
d. airbending, rainbending and earthbending

Test your knowledge with this mind-bending quiz. Add up the correct answers at the end and write your score in the box.

6) Why do Aang, Sokka and Katara go to the Northern Water Tribe?

a. to visit a friend
b. to train with master waterbenders
c. to train with master earthbenders
d. to join the tribe

7) Why does the Fire Nation steal secrets from the Great Library?

a. to learn to read
b. to set up their own library
c. to annoy the librarian
d. to harm the spirit world

8) When all the Air Nomads were killed, what did Aang become?

a. the last waterbender
b. the last airbender
c. the last earthbender
d. the last firebender

9) Why does Prince Zuko have a scar on his face?

a. he was born with it
b. it is a custom of his tribe
c. he was punished by his father
d. he had an accident

10) What does Aang's staff have hidden in it?

a. feet
b. eyes
c. teeth
d. wings

YOUR SCORE:

COMMANDER ZHAO

PROFILE: COMMANDER ZHAO

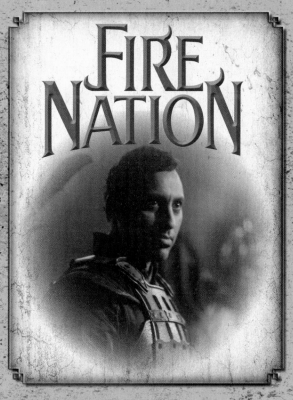

STRENGTHS:
Like Fire Lord Ozai, he's a bully who uses violence to get his way. He will attack anyone and anything – even the spirit world – to gain power for the Fire Nation and himself.

WEAKNESSES:
He is a jealous man, desperate to destroy Prince Zuko and gain the favour of the Fire Lord.

FRIENDS:
He has none! He sees himself as a leader of men and a friend to no one.

SUDOKU QUEST

Suki and her Kyoshi Warriors help Aang reach the Northern Water Tribe. You can help by filling in the grid so each line and 4x4 square contains a symbol of each element to keep the world in harmony.

AIR   WATER   EARTH   FIRE

Use your mind-bending abilities to match the right words to the gaps in these facts.

1 _____ has a nephew called Prince Zuko.

2 In the spirit world, Aang talks to a _____.

3 Sokka's favourite weapon is his _____.

4 Aang's flying bison is called _____.

5 Katara can bend _____.

6 Aang reveals he is the missing _____.

7 The Fire Nation is lead by Fire Lord _____.

8 Commander _____ dislikes Prince Zuko.

9 The Avatar was found buried in _____.

10 The Fire Nation wants to rule the _____.

ICE · ZHAO · WATER
AVATAR · DRAGON
WORLD · OZAI · IROH
BOOMERANG · APPA

PRINCESS YUE

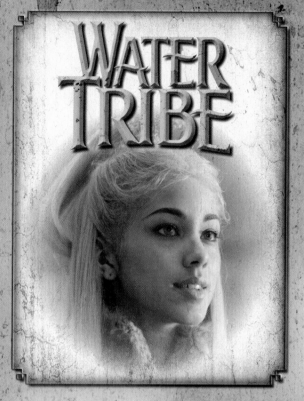

STRENGTHS:
Princess Yue is the leader of the powerful Northern Water Tribe. She also has a strong connection with the spirit world.

WEAKNESSES:
She was born weak and barely breathing, but was given life by the Moon Spirit. Her destiny is now tied to the spirit, leaving her with a life-or-death decision when the Fire Nation attacks her city.

FRIENDS:
This kind and beautiful leader has many loyal subjects. She becomes friends with Aang and Katara and grows very close to Sokka.

Aang ran away when he found out that the Avatar can't fall in love or have a family, which made him angry. He left before he was taught to bend all four elements, but he needs to master them to have his full abilities.

Aang, Sokka and Katara decide to go to Princess Yue's Northern Water Tribe, so Aang and Katara can learn from master waterbenders.

Prince Zuko tracks Aang and his friends to the Earth Kingdom. As Aang travels through the villages, he inspires confidence and bravery in all the people he meets. Zuko sees villagers removing Fire Nation banners and earthbending. He realises the Avatar's reappearance is causing a growing rebellion against the Fire Nation forces.

Iroh thinks Zuko should give up his quest and live a normal life, but Zuko's pride keeps him going. He thinks about why he was banished. After speaking out of turn to stop his friends from being sacrificed in battle, Zuko was sentenced to fight a duel. But when he saw his opponent was his father, he refused to fight. Fire Lord Ozai burned his face as punishment and banished him from the kingdom. The disgraced prince is not allowed to return until he finds the missing Avatar. Zuko is determined to complete his quest and regain his honour.

As Aang, Sokka and Katara come closer to the Northern Water Tribe, Aang visits the Northern Air Temple to speak to the spirit world. He is captured by Commander Zhao, but falls into a spiritual state of unconsciousness. The Dragon Spirit tells him the Fire Nation has stolen secrets from the Great Library, which they will use to harm the spirit world.

The Dragon Spirit warns Aang that the comet that gave the Fire Nation a moment of great power is due to come again in three years' time. Firebenders will then be able to make fire from nothing. But first Aang *must* stop them from conquering the Northern Water Tribe!

Aang then asks the Dragon Spirit about his future. The dragon tells him that Katara will be very important to him, but warns him to be careful of his feelings for her.

Aang wakes from his spiritual visit to see Commander Zhao putting a bucket of water by him. Aang doesn't bend the water and Zhao realises the boy can only bend air. He is now sure of complete victory for the Fire Nation.

A HELPFUL STRANGER?

As Commander Zhao leaves to tell Fire Lord Ozai he's captured the Avatar, a stranger enters Aang's prison cell. He wears a mask and carries swords, which he uses to free Aang. They start to escape, but as they reach the courtyard, they're surrounded by Fire Nation guards!

Aang creates strong wind currents to keep the soldiers at a distance. They retaliate with bursts of flames and the stranger uses his swords to skilfully deflect them.

A fierce battle rages, but Aang and the stranger are soon backed into a corner. The masked man then grabs Aang and puts a sword to his throat!

Zhao looks into the eyes of the masked man and realises it is Zuko. The prince will regain his honour by capturing the Avatar! But, this is not a prize Zhao will easily give up. He orders an archer to shoot at the mysterious stranger. The arrow finds its target and knocks Zuko unconscious.

Zhao can't wait to tell Fire Lord Ozai that his son is a traitor who helped the Avatar escape. But he will have to wait a little longer to bring in his prize, as Aang bends the air into swirls of clouds and escapes with Zuko.

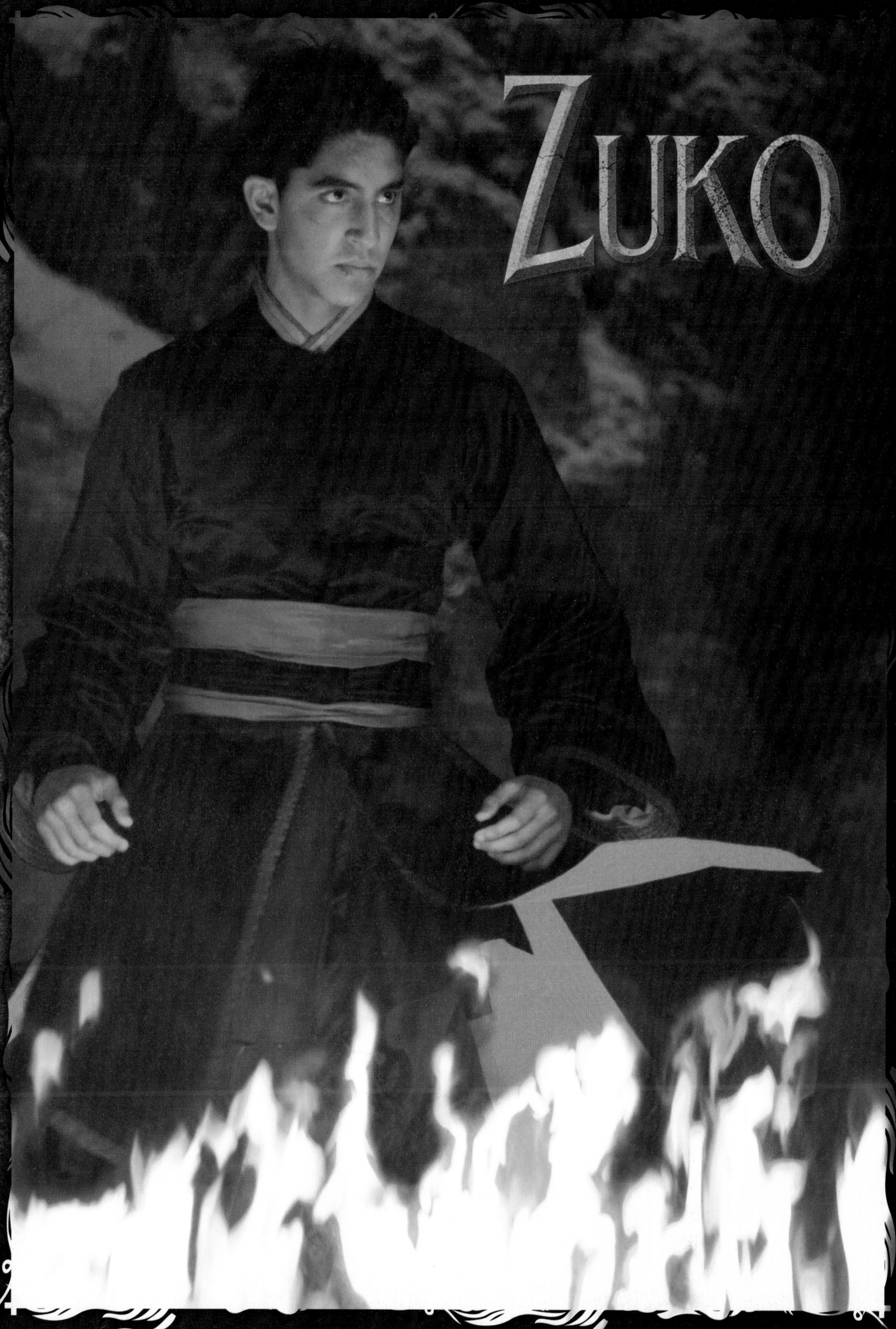
ZUKO

These pictures of Katara and Sokka look the same,
but there are 5 changes in picture 2. Can you spot them all?

WICKED WORDSEARCH

Can you find these names in the wordsearch? They can read across or down. Tick the box next to each name as you find it.

- [✓] AANG
- [✓] ZHAO
- [ ] AIRBENDER
- [✓] APPA
- [ ] LORD OZAI
- [ ] PRINCE ZUKO
- [ ] KATARA
- [ ] SOKKA
- [✓] SUKI
- [ ] UNCLE IROH

P	F	A	R	D	F	M	S	R	T	U
R	U	Z	Q	B	U	K	A	A	N	G
I	N	X	R	T	N	N	I	U	N	P
N	C	I	K	A	T	A	R	A	O	E
C	L	Q	Z	Y	T	P	B	S	T	S
E	E	A	P	P	A	O	E	T	I	O
Z	I	P	V	U	G	T	N	A	D	K
U	R	Z	A	B	F	L	D	R	K	K
K	O	H	S	U	K	I	E	U	F	A
O	H	A	R	T	X	Z	R	B	G	J
S	L	O	R	D	O	Z	A	I	Y	P

Can you match these characters to their favourite things?
Draw lines to match up the correct pairs.

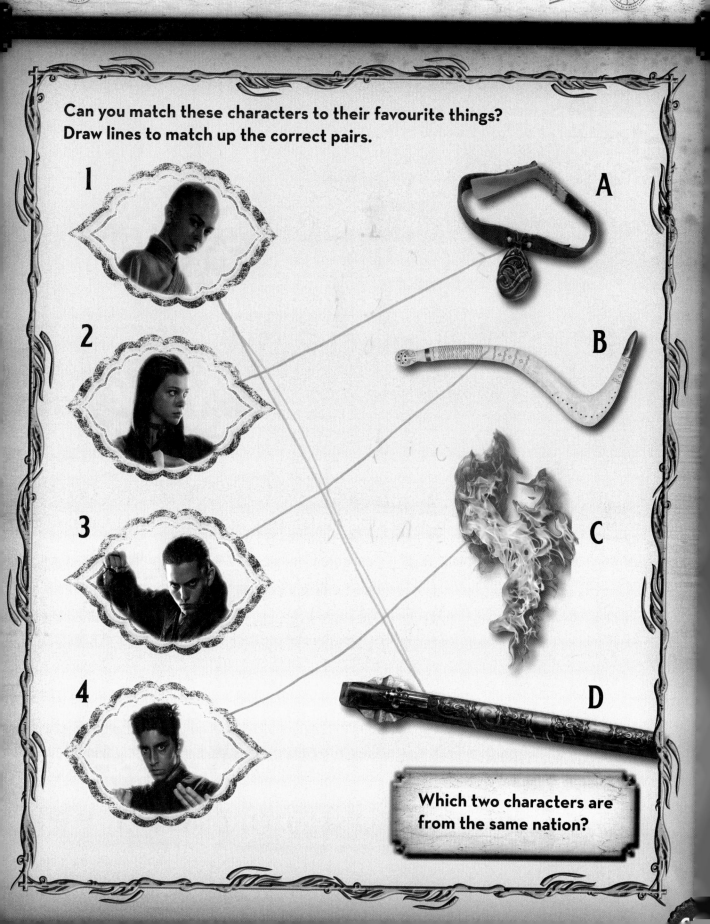

1

2

3

4

A

B

C

D

Which two characters are
from the same nation?

ULTIMATE GRID

Solve the clues to reveal the word in the blue boxes.
Then tick the box of the character it applies to.

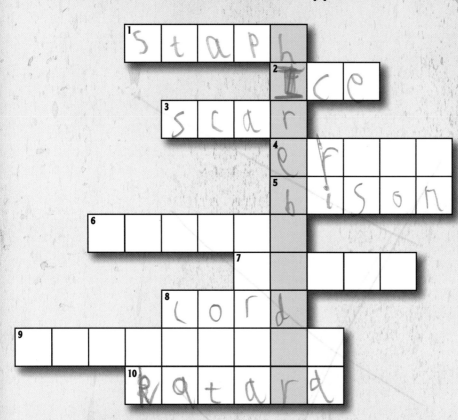

1. s t a p h
2. i c e
3. s c a r
4. f
5. b i s o n
6.
7.
8. l o r d
9.
10. k a t a r a

CLUES:

1) Aang carries a _ _ _ _ _. (5)

2) Katara can turn water into _ _ _. (3)

3) Prince Zuko has one on his face _ _ _ _. (4)

4) Aang frees a village of _ _ _ _ _ benders. (5)

5) Aang's pet Appa is a flying _ _ _ _ _. (5)

6) What is Zuko's royal rank? _ _ _ _ _ _. (5)

7) What relation is Iroh to Zuko? _ _ _ _ _. (5)

8) The Fire Nation is lead by Fire _ _ _ _ Ozai. (4)

9) Zuko's rival is _ _ _ _ _ _ _ _ _ Zhao. (9)

10) Sokka's sister is called _ _ _ _ _ _. (6)

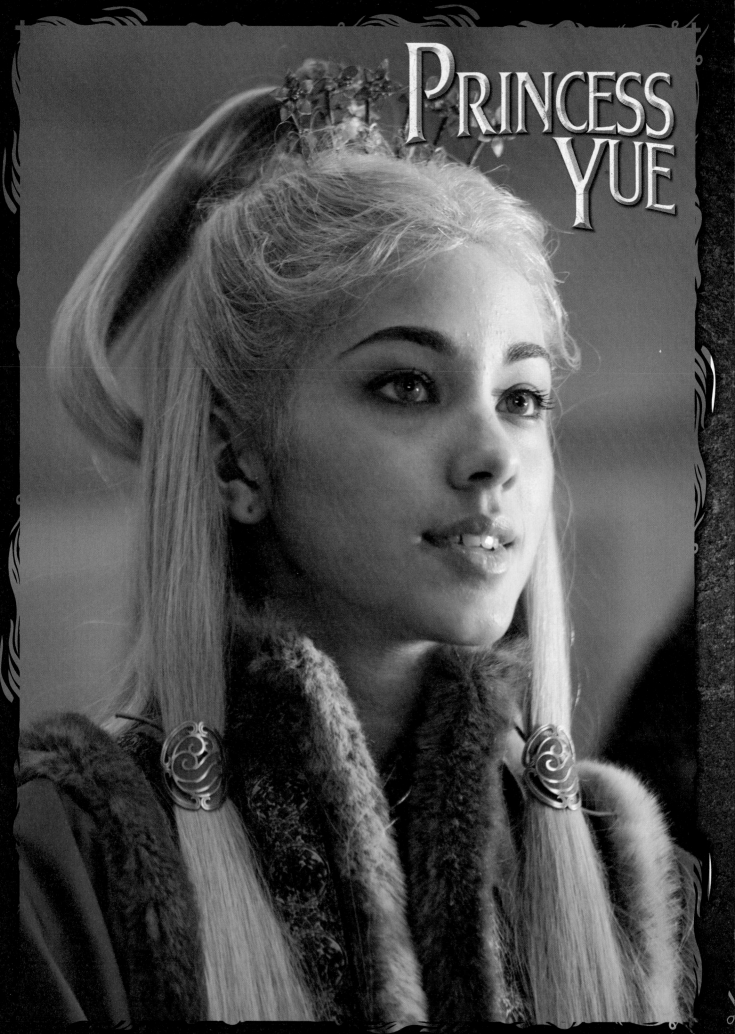

PRINCESS YUE

Would you be an airbender, an earthbender, a firebender or a waterbender? Answer these questions to find out!

1: What is your ideal job?

a. Life Guard
b. Pilot
c. Digger Driver
d. Circus Flame Thrower

2: Which outfit would you wear to a fancy dress party?

a. Pirate
b. Bird
c. Builder
d. Fireman

3: Which food do you like best?

a. fish fingers
b. chicken burger
c. jacket potato and beans
d. barbequed sausages

4: Which picture do you prefer?

a.
b.
c.
d.

5: What do you like to do on holiday?

a. go to the beach
b. take a helicopter tour
c. visit the local caves
d. drive through a desert

Mostly As
You love water! You best match the Water Tribe.

Mostly Bs
Your head is in the clouds. You best match the Air Nomads.

Mostly Cs
You're grounded. You best match the Earth Kingdom.

Mostly Ds
Are you hot-headed? You best match the Fire Nation.

ANSWERS

P15 CUNNING QUESTIONS
The hidden name is KATARA.

ICE SPHERE
WATER
AIRBENDER
LORD OZAI
TATTOO
MOTHER
SOKKA

P22 NAME GAME
The element is EARTH.

P25 TO THE RESCUE

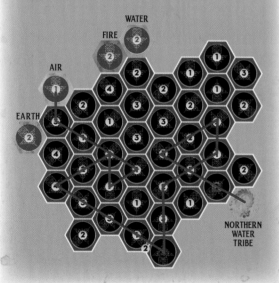

WATER
FIRE
AIR
EARTH
NORTHERN WATER TRIBE

P28-29 AANG VERSUS PRINCE ZUKO
There are 7 hidden flames.

P30-31 SPOT THE DIFFERENCE

P32 EYE FOR DETAIL

P34 CRACK THE CODE
Zuko's secret message is:
I MUST FIND THE AVATAR.

P37 A-MAZE-ING MAZE

P38 CODE NAMES
A-3 (Katara), B-2 (Aang),
C-1 (Sokka), D-4 (Zuko).

P42 FIND THE TRUE AVATAR
The true Avatar is number 4.

P45 SOKKA SILHOUETTES
Sokka's silhouette is number 3.

P48-49 MIND-BENDING QUIZ
1) C   3) B   5) A   7) D   9) C
2) A   4) A   6) B   8) B   10) D

P52 SUDOKU QUEST

P53 FILL IN THE BLANKS
1) IROH   6) AVATAR
2) DRAGON   7) OZAI
3) BOOMERANG   8) ZHAO
4) APPA   9) ICE
5) WATER   10) WORLD

P61 SPOT THE DIFFERENCE

P62 WICKED WORDSEARCH

P63 LINE 'EM UP!
1) D 2) A 3) B 4) C. Sokka and
Katara are from the same nation.

P64 ULTIMATE GRID

1) STAFF
2) ICE
3) SCAR
4) EARTH
5) BISON
6) PRINCE
7) UNCLE
8) LORD
9) COMMANDER
10) KATARA

The blue word applies to Prince Zuko.

FOUR KINGDOMS

one dest